DISNEY
Sofia the First

A Day at Royal Prep

bendon®

81327-TG Sofia the First Super Book to Color

Welcome to the family, Sofia!

Which picture of Sofia is different?

Your
Answer:

King Roland says there will be a ball in Sofia's honor.

The king gives Sofia the Amulet of Avalor.
She promises to always wear it!

Cedric, The Royal Sorcerer

Cedric wants Sofia's magic amulet.

"The amulet is so pretty, Sofia. May I hold it?"
asks Cedric.

The Magic Amulet
Find the best words to complete the rhyme.

For each deed performed, for better or

_____.

Which word comes next?

Word   Work   Worse

A power is granted, a blessing or

_____.

Which word comes next?

Care   Curse   Call

"Oh, Merlin's mushrooms!" says Cedric.

Sofia asks Cedric for a dancing spell.

Cedric wants to trick Sofia and take the amulet.

Sofia hopes the spell works!

Draw what Cedric is thinking about.

Sofia dances with the king.

Princess Sofia wakes up.

Time to get dressed.

© Disney

Baileywick takes Sofia to breakfast.

So many choices!

Time for school.

Connect the dots to complete the flying horse.

Headmistresses Flora, Fauna, and Merryweather

Amber's best friends—Clio and Hildegard

Hurry to class.

Every princess must know how to curtsy.

Arts & Crafts

Draw what Sofia is painting.

Sofia makes friends at Royal Prep.

© Disney

Professor Popov's Dance Class

© Disney

Recess!

Amber and Clio share a secret.

Hildegard gets an "A" in Fan Fluttering.

© Disney

Time to Study

Be careful, Sofia!

Magic Class

© Disney

Learning to be a princess is not easy!

Home Sweet Home

Find and circle 7 items that begin with the letter B.

Possible answers: ball, barrel, bee, basket, book, bird, broom, banner

A Royal Tea Party

Oops!

Amber wonders if Sofia will ever be a real princess.

Baileywick announces that dinner is served.

Sofia has so much to learn!

"How was your day, dear?"

Sofia misses her village friends.

© Disney

Ruby and Jade

A Royal Makeover

Homework with Vivian—Build a Dream Castle

Draw your own Dream Castle.

Best Friends Forever!

Crackle!

New Friends

Crackle's Special Talent

The Prince and Princesses of Enchancia!

© Disney